Co-occurring Disorders Series

UNDERSTANDING POST-TRAUMATIC STRESS DISORDER AND ADDICTION

Revised

Katie Evans, Ph.D.

HAZELDEN

FORMERLY THE DUAL DIAGNOSIS SERIES

Hazelden
Center City, Minnesota 55012-0176

1-800-328-9000
1-651-213-4590 (Fax)
www.hazelden.org

ISBN 13: 978-1-59285-025-9

Editor's note
This material was written to educate individuals about chemical dependency
and mental illness. It is not intended as a substitute for professional medical
or psychiatric care.

Any stories or case studies that may be used in this material are com-
posites of many individuals. Names and details have been changed to protect
identities.

Cover design by Lightbourne
Interior design by Lightbourne

Dedicated to my children, Callie and Casey. I love you well.

CONTENTS

INTRODUCTION

This was written for you, the person suffering from two diseases: chemical dependency and post-traumatic stress disorder. You may be surprised to learn that post-traumatic stress disorder (PTSD) is a disease just like cancer, diabetes, or many other medical problems. Maybe you're reading this because you or someone close to you thinks that your flashbacks (involuntary reliving in your mind of events that took place in the past), intrusive thoughts, persistent tension, detachment from feelings, or avoidance of certain activities are making your life (or his or hers) unmanageable. Perhaps a psychiatrist, physician, psychologist, or other qualified professional has told you that you suffer from post-traumatic stress disorder. You may be one of the thousands of recovering alcoholics or addicts who are working a Twelve Step program of recovery and yet continue to suffer the aftereffects of trauma—having difficulty living life on life's terms. This may have led you to contemplate taking that first drink or pill. You may even have thought of ending your life, thinking that the program is just not working for you.

True post-traumatic stress disorder—persistent stress that results from physical or emotional injury—is a diagnosis that only a qualified professional can make. If you have not had such a diagnosis, see a professional—don't assume that because you are often anxious or feel under stress that you have PTSD. It resembles other major anxiety disorders (which are written about separately in this series of pamphlets on dual disorders), but there are important differences.

This pamphlet was written to help you work a combined recovery program for both your chemical dependency and your post-traumatic stress disorder. Information about your dual disorders and some practical suggestions for working a combined program will be provided. It is hoped that this material will help you to develop and maintain pro-recovery attitudes and to take action to get out of the problem and into the solution. This pamphlet is not a quick fix or a substitute for professional assistance. It is a source of ideas and tools that are meant to complement other parts of your recovery program.

The term "dual disorders" refers to two coexisting disorders. This pamphlet will discuss both chemical addiction and PTSD. It will focus on the need to work a recovery program that addresses both problems at the same time. People who have been traumatized can become chemically dependent and people who are chemically dependent can suffer from the experience of serious trauma.

The term "post-traumatic stress disorder" is used in a broad sense. These are not only survivors of war, kidnapping, rape, attempted murder, or a natural disaster, but are also survivors of such childhood trauma as physical and emotional neglect, physical abuse, or incest. The effects of serious trauma—trauma that diminishes your sense of safety in the world—are discussed here. If left untreated, these effects can last far beyond early recovery. PTSD can dilute the quality of your recovery from chemical dependency, lead to a relapse into drinking or using, or even make suicide seem attractive.

You may have symptoms and problems that are similar to those of PTSD if you are actively using or are in early recovery from addiction. Using mood-altering chemicals for long periods can actually increase your feelings of anxiety. Part of the increase is your body's response to prolonged use of the chemicals; part is your attempt to "manage the unmanageable." You are trying to remain in control, not only of your chemical use but also of people, places, and things. You may have amnesia due to blackouts, a lack of interest in activities other than using, or a restricted range of feelings. You may have distressing memories of your behavior such as "morning-after remorse." You may have strong memories that feel like flashbacks. Even as you enter recovery, you are likely to experience some of these problems. Some represent post-acute withdrawal symptoms; some signal the breakdown of denial—you now realize what your drinking and using have done to your life—and some represent the effects of the chemicals on your brain and your life.

You may feel jumpy, anxious, unsettled. You may frantically try to avoid thoughts of using—or situations and activities associated with using—during the first weeks and months of abstinence. But these difficulties will gradually disappear once you are free of chemicals, maintain sobriety, and work a Twelve Step program of recovery.

By learning how to work a program for both your chemical dependency and your PTSD, you will begin to experience the serenity that others working a Twelve Step program have found. And you will experience the Promises offered in the Big Book of Alcoholics Anonymous (AA).*

---

* The Promises of the rewards that come with working a recovery program appear throughout *Alcoholics Anonymous* (published by Alcoholics Anonymous World Services, Inc., New York, 3d ed., 1976); see especially the last paragraph on page 83 through line 15 on page 84.

Appendix A, page 33, contains questions that you can answer to increase your understanding of the material in this pamphlet. Appendix B, page 35, provides a chart to help you develop a daily schedule of activities. Appendix C, page 37, is a list of useful Twelve Step slogans.

THE DISEASES OF CHEMICAL DEPENDENCY AND POST-TRAUMATIC STRESS DISORDER

Chemical dependency and PTSD are diseases. To recover from them, you must work a program with specific steps. Look at the following table. It lists the causes and main symptoms of these diseases and it gives the steps necessary for recovery. This table and the discussion that follows it will help you understand your dual disorders and your recovery program.

COMPARISON OF THE DISEASE OF CHEMICAL DEPENDENCY AND POST-TRAUMATIC STRESS DISORDER

Factor	Chemical Dependency	Post-traumatic Stress Disorder
Causes	• alcohol and other drug use	• traumatic events, including war, rape, and accidents; also abandonment and abuse by family of origin

Factor	Chemical Dependency	Post-traumatic Stress Disorder
Causes (continued)	• changes in brain chemistry and brain function	• changes in brain chemistry and brain function
	• hereditary and environmental factors	• inability to escape trauma that occurred at a young age or that was life threatening as well as repeated and often pro-longed; lack of social support and validation
Symptoms	• tolerance, withdrawal, progression	• persistent bodily anxiety
	• denial	• guilt, self-blame, avoidance
	• loss of control	• re-experiencing of trauma (flashbacks)
	• continued use despite negative consequences	• avoidance of feared situations and psychological numbing
	• physical, interpersonal, social, occupa-tional, spiritual problems	• physical, interpersonal, social, occupa-tional, spiritual problems

Factor	Chemical Dependency	Post-traumatic Stress Disorder
Symptoms (continued)	• hospitalization, imprisonment, insanity, death	• hospitalization, imprisonment, self-harm, suicide
Recovery Program	• abstinence • AA, NA, CA* attendance • sponsor • Step work • reading the Big Book • helping others	• social support • skills to provide safety and care for yourself • working through the trauma • medication and/or psychotherapy • hospitalization or treatment program

* Alcoholics Anonymous, Narcotics Anonymous, Cocaine Anonymous

The Disease of Chemical Dependency

If you drink alcohol or take other drugs that have abuse potential, you can start a process of change in your brain chemistry. Eventually, the result can be addiction. If you have a family history of alcoholism or other addictions, the chances are greater that this process will occur in you. *Tolerance* means that you need to take increasing amounts of a substance to achieve the same effects. It is one sign that the physical process of addiction has begun. Another sign is *withdrawal,* which means that after you stop drinking or using, you may feel very uncomfortable. Physical, mental, and emotional problems can develop. Withdrawal can be life threatening, especially with alcohol, tranquilizers, and other sedatives, and requires medical management.

Other key symptoms of the disease of chemical dependency are *loss of control* and *continued use of chemicals* despite the serious problems they cause. Perhaps you have tried to cut down on your use—or even to quit—but you cannot. Maybe you find that you keep drinking or using more than you had planned. Another symptom is *progression.* This refers to the fact that this disease gets worse over time, never better. Once you are a pickle, you can no longer be a cucumber. Maybe you find that you have become so preoccupied with chemical use that using has become the most important thing in your life—more important than other activities and people. Perhaps you continue to use despite damage to your body, fights at home, problems on the job, legal problems, or loss of faith and hope. These are all symptoms of the disease of chemical dependency.

Denial is strong in the disease of chemical dependency. No doubt you felt denial before you entered recovery. You have a disease that says you don't have a disease! Blaming others is part of denial, and so is making excuses for your drinking and using and the problems they have caused.

Chemical dependency is a *progressive disease*—that is, it gets worse with time if you don't treat it. It is a chronic, fatal disease that has no cure. But you can experience a remission—a reduction of your symptoms. Recovery starts with abstinence from all mood-altering chemicals. You can get the support and guidance you need to promote your recovery by attending Alcoholics Anonymous or similar Twelve Step self-help groups and by working with a Twelve Step sponsor or support person. Working the Steps can lead you to accept your disease. It can help you repair the emotional and spiritual damage caused by your drinking and using. Last but not least, it can help you grow and feel comfortable and happy with yourself.

The Disease of

Post-traumatic Stress Disorder

Something bad has happened to you. It is serious and upsetting, and it produces feelings of intense fear and helplessness. Such an event can cause a post-traumatic stress disorder (PTSD).

One kind of trauma is obvious—you know exactly what happened—for example, taking part in a war; being raped; being victimized by some other violent crime; surviving a plane crash; living through serious physical or sexual abuse.

Another kind of trauma is subtle. The problem is that you do *not* know, or cannot remember, what happened. Generally, your parents (or significant others) neglected you physically and emotionally. They did not give you sufficient support and accept you for who you were or meet your needs for safety, love, and self-esteem. They were not there for you.

Often these two kinds of trauma go together. For example, one parent may be physically or sexually abusive. The other parent may emotionally abandon the child by not protecting him or her from this trauma.

When PTSD affects you, how much it affects you and the ways it affects you can vary. Sometimes the symptoms begin immediately after the traumatic event. Sometimes they don't occur until weeks or months or years later. When they do finally occur, it is usually in response to a series of stressful events, to losses, or to the recurrence of situations that seem like the original traumatic event.

You may experience a variety of physical signs of PTSD. You may sleep poorly and have nightmares; startle easily; have trouble concentrating; feel irritable or angry without reasonable cause; have headaches, stomachaches, and dizziness; be persistently tense and anxious. It's as if your body were constantly on "red alert."

With PTSD you may try to avoid thoughts, activities, people, or situations that remind you of the trauma. Perhaps you can't recall the event or you may lose your memory for periods of time. You may feel distant and detached from others. Your normal activities may now hold little interest or pleasure. Perhaps you can hardly feel love, tenderness, or intimacy.

Some people who have PTSD re-experience the traumatic event from time to time. You may recall the trauma in your dreams or even while walking down the street. If you have flashbacks, you act as if you were right back in the traumatic situation.

Other symptoms are also associated with PTSD. They can include mood swings, depression, and rage. Some may involve impulsive behavior, such as suddenly changing jobs, residences, or friends. Some may be connected to harmful behavior, such as cutting yourself. You may experience guilt and low self-esteem, wondering why you survived and others didn't or why you did the things you did or whether you are to blame for what happened. You may constantly feel helpless and out of control. You may think you fit in with no one. You may not be sure what you believe, think, and feel. You may not know what normal is.

Perhaps it is hard for you to hold on to a job or to maintain successful and healthy long-term relationships. A history of unpredictable, threatening, or unsupportive relationships with a parent or spouse can leave you with serious issues about intimacy and trust. As human beings, we require love, nurturing, and emotional support. But to receive such support, we must trust and be willing to be vulnerable. For the survivor of trauma, however, being trusting and vulnerable is often associated with feeling out of control and unsafe.

You may constantly scan your surroundings or monitor your feelings and thoughts, always alert to signs of danger and abandonment. You may block all feelings or put yourself in dangerous situations to distract yourself and avoid emotional pain. You may be ever ready to escape from any situation that triggers distress or guilt and blame yourself as if it were your fault that you were traumatized. Such feelings are a key part of PTSD.

Having PTSD can mean that your life is like a roller-coaster ride in hell. One minute you feel frozen; the next minute you feel flooded with fear, pain, and anger. At times you feel you are life's victim, but then you struggle fiercely to maintain control over yourself and other people. Danger is always lurking, and you are compelled to organize your life around being safe.

People with PTSD can have a number of related disorders and problems. This is partly because PTSD can show up in different ways and partly because the extent of the PTSD depends on several factors. Serious PTSD is more likely to develop if the trauma was prolonged, life threatening, unpredictable, repeated, or caused by people rather than by natural or unavoidable disasters. There are other contributing factors to serious PTSD: Did the trauma happen at a young age? Could you resist or escape? Was there a lack of support and validation from others? Those who experienced serious trauma as an adult are more likely to suffer from recurrent major depressions or an anxiety disorder as well as PTSD. Those who experienced serious trauma as a child, especially physical or sexual abuse, may also have borderline personality disorder or multiple personality disorder as well as PTSD.

A person with PTSD is likely to develop chemical dependency. This is because those who caused the physical or sexual abuse in childhood, or the neglect and abandonment, were often chemically dependent themselves. You may have inherited a predisposition to chemical dependency and were exposed to parents who abused drugs and alcohol. Using mood-altering substances can help you numb the pain, sleep through the night, and stifle the flashbacks. But they can quickly become part of the problem. Being drunk or high can actually make you more likely to feel depressed or anxious. It can contribute to dangerous, impulsive actions and bring up more bad memories. And using mood-altering chemicals will interfere with therapy and other activities designed to help you recover from PTSD. These drugs keep you from learning new coping skills and working through the trauma.

Pete's Story

Pete was drafted into the Army in 1969. Six months later he found himself in a Vietnam jungle. Like many nineteen-year-olds in the Vietnam war, Pete experienced the brutality of combat. "Kill or be killed" was the only reality he knew. To escape the reality of the war, Pete would drink until he could drop facedown in the sand and sleep. After four months of jungle combat, Pete's unit was transferred to a bomb factory, where he helped assemble bombs. He said that when his bombs exploded, they couldn't tell the difference between soldiers and innocent bystanders. Pete began to have vivid nightmares. They woke him up four or five times a week in a cold sweat, full of terror.

After returning from Vietnam, Pete joined a veterans' support group to try to deal with the bad dreams and flashbacks he was having. He listened to other vets discuss killing women and children, but somehow he felt his experience wasn't as bad as that of the other members of the group and he didn't talk much. The nightmares continued, so did the intrusive daytime memories of making bombs and the visions of bombs exploding.

Pete's drinking continued and he began to smoke marijuana. Still he found it hard to relax. His wife expressed concern about his heavy use of drugs and alcohol. Conflicts increased. Ultimately Pete's marriage ended in divorce.

After the divorce, Pete decided he needed a change of scenery. He moved to a small college town and began to work on a degree in psychology. It was during a psychology lab that Pete met Megan. Six months later they got married. Soon Megan noted how often she felt Pete was emotionally distant and unsupportive. She discussed this with Pete, but eventually the discussions would turn into arguments and Pete would angrily drive off to a local tavern and drink until closing.

Megan was pregnant when she asked him to go to counseling with her. His drinking came up, but the focus was on communication skills. Pete and Megan continued to fight. They seemed to grow further apart after the birth of their son. One night, after Pete had drunk too much, he came home and got into a fight with Megan. It turned violent. Pete began shoving Megan against the wall, slapping her, and breaking furniture. The following day Megan took their baby and moved out. She started divorce proceedings and filed a restraining order against Pete. Angry, guilty, and alone, Pete dropped out of college and began to drift from place to place. He tried to stay drunk most of the time—it drowned out the bad memories of the war and his two failed marriages.

Two days after his twenty-sixth birthday, Pete was arrested for drunk driving and ordered into chemical dependency treatment. He stayed for ten days. The anxiety and paranoia grew more intense each day. Pete began to fear that if he couldn't drink or use drugs to help cope with his pain, he would have to kill himself. On the tenth day of his rehabilitation program, Pete got into a fight with a counselor and was kicked out of treatment. On his twelfth day of sobriety, Pete found himself alone in his apartment, looking at his pistol and thinking about ending it all. Death seemed the only solution to his problems.

In a last desperate attempt for help, Pete called the local AA crisis hotline. He talked for almost an hour to a woman who really seemed to understand how he felt. The woman gave him the name of a counselor who specialized in working with people who have dual disorders. Pete called the counselor and got an appointment for the next day. She also gave him information on two dual diagnosis AA meetings in his neighborhood.

Immediately, Pete began individual counseling with the therapist to deal with both his chemical dependency and his post-traumatic stress disorder. In addition, he joined a group of men who were also working on relapse and other psychological problems. By working a combined recovery program, Pete was able for the first time to stay sober one day at a time as he began the road to recovery from his two diseases of chemical dependency and post-traumatic stress disorder.

Recovery Is Possible

Recovery from PTSD is possible. It starts when you build and use a social support system. It helps to learn and use new skills that provide safety and meet your needs. Working through the trauma in a safe way will assure that you get off the roller coaster. Certain medications can also help, as can therapy with a qualified professional.

Recovering from either the disease of chemical dependency or post-traumatic stress disorder is difficult.

Recovering from *both* diseases can pose a special challenge when you are prone to (a) the urge to use and (b) mood swings (being emotionally frozen or flooded). But understanding your coexisting disorders, and accepting them, mean the beginning of your journey of recovery.

HOW TO WORK
A COMBINED PROGRAM
OF RECOVERY

This section discusses good ways to work a combined program of recovery for your dual disorders of chemical dependency and PTSD.

Acceptance

It is crucial that you accept the dual diseases of chemical dependency and PTSD. Without acceptance, you are likely to remain trapped by the idea that you are weak or bad. You might still think that you could get better if only you tried hard enough and pulled yourself up by your bootstraps. If you review the causes and symptoms of both disorders in the preceding section, and if you can see how they apply to you, you will begin to realize that you are ill, not bad. Acceptance of your disorders is the first step in recovery.

Abstinence

Dual recovery begins with abstinence from addictive, mood-altering chemicals. Using alcohol, tranquilizers, marijuana, or other mood-altering chemicals will make both diseases worse. Without abstinence, you will not be able to begin a true dual recovery program. You will continue to experience the serious consequences of your addiction on your body, mind, and behavior. While you use drugs and alcohol, your anxiety will increase and it will be more and more difficult to deal with your other symptoms. Denial and watchfulness will increase. *Abstinence* can help you develop new solutions to your old problems.

Being a Survivor

Begin to think of yourself as a *survivor,* not as a victim. There are a number of benefits. It will help you to respect the fact that you have the right to feel safe. You will begin to see your symptoms not as faults but as unique and creative attempts to cope with overwhelming events. You will begin to acknowledge that in some ways you have special experiences and strengths that can be assets if properly understood and complemented by new skills and new thinking. And you can begin to move from feeling helpless to feeling a new sense of self and newfound faith.

An Active Recovery Program

Just as your dual diseases have dominated your life and made it unmanageable, you now need to make a priority of working an *active dual recovery program.* A recovery program means that you take active steps. Abstaining from chemicals and striving to keep safe is a good start. In a word, recovery is a program of action!

Support from Others

Attending Twelve Step meetings, such as Alcoholics Anonymous (AA), Narcotics Anonymous (NA), or Cocaine Anonymous (CA), will serve as a key support as you stay clean and sober and work with your PTSD. Eventually, you can supplement your program by attending support groups for your specific situation, such as Adult Children of Alcoholics or incest-survivor support groups. At these meetings you will hear others share their experiences, strengths, and hopes. You will find fellowship with those who have struggled, and still struggle, with many of the same issues you face. You can talk honestly about your problems and feelings and efforts to recover, without fear of judgment, ridicule, or criticism. The open, caring, and nonjudgmental atmosphere of Twelve Step meetings will help you combat your feelings of being bad and shameful. At meetings, you can practice expressing your thoughts and feelings directly in a safe place. Members may offer supportive comments after the meeting and offer to talk with you on the phone. Most areas have different groups meeting at different times, so you will always have a place to go for support.

Besides this general support, *obtaining a sponsor* is helpful. Sponsors are members of a Twelve Step group who act as mentors and guides. They help you learn about Twelve Step programs and support you during those tough times when you feel alone and believe that nobody understands how you feel. If you experienced serious physical or sexual abuse, you may feel safer if your sponsor is not the gender of the person who abused you.

Trusting others tends to be a problem for survivors of trauma. While trust often comes slowly, sometimes survivors trust too soon, too intensely. We recommend that you go slowly and safely as you get support from others.

Taking Care of Yourself

It is important to develop skills to take care of yourself. Especially if you suffered childhood trauma, your emotional, physical, and psychological needs may not have been met. It is time to learn how to take care of your basic needs. *Maintaining good nutrition* can make a difference. A good start is to develop and stick to a food plan that includes proper amounts of the basic food groups. Eating right will help replenish nutrients that have been depleted by chemicals and stress and will give you the physical energy, mental clarity, and emotional stamina you need.

Developing a weekly schedule is a good idea. Survivors often have difficulty getting organized. With a schedule, you'll have external structure to help you to keep a good balance of work, play, and social activities as well as to ensure an active recovery program. Set aside time one day each week to write your weekly plan. Fill it in for Sunday through Saturday, from 8 A.M. to midnight, blocking out times for your activities. Be sure to fill any holes in your schedule that are left open. Appendix B contains a sample blank schedule. Do not overschedule.

Go bowling, take a brisk walk, or ride a bicycle (even a stationary one at home). These *physical activities* will help you relax and will promote a sense of well-being. They provide alternatives to drinking and using. Exercise also helps repair the distorted brain chemistry that can result from your dual diseases.

Increasing your ability to be *assertive* is a useful and effective self-care skill. While it is difficult for survivors to identify and manage intense feelings, they find it even harder to express them to others directly and appropriately. Earlier you may have had to suppress or deny your feelings, needs, and wants, or you may have learned that being direct about them got you disapproval, discounting, or punishment. Your parents may have modeled only aggressive, dominant behavior or meek, submissive behavior. Learning to be more assertive will give you ways to feel safe and comfortable with your feelings. Expressing yourself honestly and assertively will improve the quality of all your relationships. In turn, you will avoid the effects of stuffing your emotions, a situation that could trigger a relapse into drinking and using. Many self-help books are available at your local bookstore to help you become more assertive. Show up and speak up!

Using alcohol and drugs can distort your thinking. It causes denial and other attitudes that make it difficult for you to see how your behavior is hurting yourself. Being a survivor can also distort your thinking. Survivors sometimes think of themselves as victims and tend to develop a view of the world that says they are in constant danger and at the mercy of other persons, places, or things. The constant vigilance that results is often accompanied by a constant readiness to take any action to avoid dreaded situations, even when these situations are basically harmless. Besides being constantly on alert, you can also come to believe that you are a bad person—unworthy, incapable, and incompetent. You may discount your achievements and focus only on your problems. You may have victim-stance thinking.

Thinking constructively will help you with your dual recovery. Members of Twelve Step groups use certain phrases, called slogans, to express helpful ways to look at themselves and the world. "One day at a time" and "Progress not perfection" are some examples. *Saying slogans* to yourself when you feel wound up, overwhelmed, or guilty can help you cultivate acceptance and serenity.

Remind yourself that you are a survivor, not a victim, and that you are someone with special coping skills and strengths. You as a survivor are on the road to becoming a thriver.

You can also practice positive *self-talk* or *affirmations*. You might catch yourself during the day doing something positive and say to yourself, "Good work!" Remember, too, that small things done reasonably well, not just major triumphs, can represent good work. With the help of a friend, sponsor, or therapist, you can also develop a list of personal assets and accomplishments. You might review your list and the Twelve Step slogans in appendix C, on page 37, once or twice a day in order to practice constructive thinking. At first this might seem artificial, but with time you will probably experience a slow but sure change in your thinking.

Survivor Work

Another part of your recovery from PTSD is *working through* your traumatic experiences. This means slowly and carefully allowing yourself to re-experience the trauma in a safe environment by talking about it and remembering it. Survivor work can give you a clearer picture of how the trauma has affected your life. This work usually begins after the first year of recovery.

It is important that you gradually expose yourself to the memories or situations that trigger your anxiety, something best done with the assistance of a qualified professional. To avoid these memories or situations is to let them maintain their power over your life. Eventually you must face them. In doing so, you will move from the there and then to the here and now.

But I can't, you think. Remember that you now have others to support you. You have learned new ways to take care of yourself, including constructive thinking. Remember, too, that you can do it at your own pace, step by step.

If you like to read, *reading books and articles* about trauma, dysfunctional families, codependency, and related themes is a good start. You will get a framework for understanding your experience. *Telling your story* is another good way to do this work. Talk with someone who is supportive or keep a journal. *Becoming aware of old patterns* that you still repeat will set the stage for making constructive changes. Take this slow. Recovery is a process, not an event.

A fundamental issue to work through is called survivor guilt and shame. Most survivors feel guilty about what happened, what they did to survive, or even the fact that they *did* survive. You must come to believe that you did not cause the events that you experienced and that you did the best you could to cope with what happened. You truly are a miracle.

Psychotherapy

You can take some of the actions outlined above by yourself. But psychotherapy with a qualified professional can boost your dual recovery. A therapist or counselor can give you support, help you develop self-care skills, and guide you with your survivor work. As you select a counselor, keep in mind that survivors of trauma, especially childhood trauma like incest, are often more comfortable working with a counselor whose gender is opposite that of the perpetrator. A counselor who is familiar with post-traumatic stress disorder *and* with recovery from chemical dependency will help you establish a solid recovery program. Call treatment center referral lines to get the names of therapists who have the skills to help you. Seek a therapist who has dual diagnosis expertise who can mentor and guide you on your road to recovery.

THREE

MEDICATION

PTSD is a disease and sometimes certain kinds of medication can be helpful if used briefly for acute symptoms. When flashbacks are especially severe, when your anxiety is particularly disabling, or when you are feeling profound depression, medication can help. It's difficult to work a program when your symptoms overwhelm you. Appropriate medication can complement the other strategies talked about in this pamphlet.

FOUR

SPECIAL CONCERNS FOR PEOPLE WHO ARE CHEMICALLY DEPENDENT

Recovering from chemical dependency presents a problem to people considering the use of medication for their PTSD. If recovery requires abstinence from mood-altering chemicals, how can you justify taking medications used for PTSD that are mood-altering?

Remember that you have coexisting disorders, chemical dependency and PTSD. Try to distinguish between a chemical you abuse and a medication you take for disease. Recall, too, that Alcoholics Anonymous and similar recovery groups have no official position on such medication; rather, they urge their members to consult physicians. Ask around in your Twelve Step meetings about physicians who are sensitive to the special needs of those in recovery. Discuss your addiction honestly with your physician; explain that you are concerned about the possibility of abusing any medication. But as you will see below, a number of the medications used for PTSD have no abuse potential.

Special Concerns for the Survivor

You can experience a number of symptoms if you suffer from PTSD. You can be anxious, depressed, and/or have flashbacks. Be sure to tell your physician that these are all symptoms of PTSD and not separate problems; otherwise, you run the risk of getting a separate prescription for each symptom. Avoid taking multiple medications for multiple symptoms. If this happened, you would not receive overall treatment for your underlying condition but only symptomatic treatment. You would probably continue to need medications for any relief at all, and your relief might be only minimal. This is costly. It exposes you to the risk of undesirable drug interactions. At best it is a temporary solution, at worst ineffective. Do the best you can to insist on a thorough diagnostic evaluation and on referral for treatment beyond just medication.

Types of Medication

Medical professionals use a variety of medications to treat PTSD. Some are safe for the recovering person and some are a risk to your recovery and may lead to relapse. Antidepressants, the beta-blocker antihypertensives, and the antipsychotics all have little abusive potential and are not addictive.

The risky, addictive medications are the tranquilizers and another class of drugs known as sedative-hypnotics. Examples are Valium and Xanax. Such medications have effects that are similar to those of alcohol. In fact, they act like alcohol. They can be abused and can contribute to serious addiction.

Headaches and other bodily aches affect some survivors as a result of their constant stress. Painkillers that have a narcotic base are addictive. Avoid these medications. Use other means to deal with your pain and stress, such as those outlined in the section "How to Work a Combined Program of Recovery."

When your physician prescribes medication for you,

always remember to take it exactly as directed. And be sure you talk to your doctor before you make any changes in your medication. Suddenly stopping or starting or otherwise changing medications can be dangerous.

Georgia's Story

Georgia was only four years old when her stepfather first began to touch her private parts. She thought it must be wrong because her stepfather insisted that it be just *their* secret. Georgia was to tell *no one* about it.

By the time Georgia was nine, her stepfather had had sexual intercourse with her. He would buy her presents and take her on special outings, just the two of them. Often the outings were ruined when he wanted to play the "touching game" that ultimately led to intercourse.

Georgia began to resent her mother for not protecting her. Even though Georgia never told her mother about the abuse, she felt her mother should have known and should have stopped it.

At age eleven, Georgia began drinking. She found her stepfather's sexual abuse easier to deal with when she was drinking. Since her stepfather found her more cooperative when she was drinking, he supplied her with all the alcohol she wanted. By age fourteen, Georgia began skipping school and running away. A year later, she had left her home and school for good and was living with some other teenage girls.

Georgia began having nightmares when she was sixteen. She would dream of men standing over her with guns dripping with blood. Sometimes during waking hours she would have flashes of different scenes of her stepfather's abuse of her. Eventually during this year, she attempted suicide for the first time—a large amount of whiskey and some sleeping pills. Over the next ten years, Georgia was hospitalized six times for attempted suicide. Each time she got a new medication. Georgia's drug and alcohol abuse seldom came up in discussions with her doctors or other hospital staff. Most hospitalizations focused on her self-destructive behavior—cutting herself and attempting suicide.

At age twenty-eight, Georgia was hospitalized for the seventh time, in a psychiatric facility. Finally she was referred to a dual diagnosis program. At the time of admission, she was on six different medications: Xanax, Valium, Desyrel, Dalmane, Effexor, and lithium.

This time Georgia was taken off all medication except Effexor. She began attending chemical dependency counseling groups, where she honestly discussed her use of alcohol and drugs. She began working the Twelve Steps of Alcoholics Anonymous, learned assertiveness skills, and began survivor work.

As Georgia began to think of herself not as a victim but as a survivor, and as she got free of mood-altering chemicals, life became more pleasant. One day at a time Georgia found faith that her life could improve. Learning that she was an "addicted survivor" helped her take one step at a time on her path of dual recovery.

IN CLOSING

I hope you can now see that you suffer from two diseases: chemical dependency and post-traumatic stress disorder.

You are not responsible for having them or the problems they bring to your life. But you *are* responsible for finding *solutions* to those problems.

Working a combined program of recovery for your dual disorders can guide you out of the problem and into the solution, one day at a time.

COMING TO KNOW
YOUR DISORDERS

Use this worksheet to help apply the information in this pamphlet to your life. After you read the pamphlet, take some time to write down your answers for each of the following items. You may also wish to review your answers with your sponsor, your therapist, a friend, or an appropriate family member.

1. Write down at least five signs or problems that indicate that you suffer from the disease of chemical dependency.

2. Write down at least five signs or problems that indicate that you suffer from the disease of PTSD.

3. Explain why you are "sick getting well," not "bad getting good," and why you are not responsible for having the diseases of chemical dependency and PTSD.

4. List any major reservations you may have about accepting your two diseases. For each reservation, list one thing you could think or do to deal with this reservation.

5. List any major roadblocks that might stop you from making active recovery a priority in your life. Consider such obstacles as money and time, an unsupportive spouse, and your own attitudes. (For

example, you don't believe recovery will make a difference.) For each roadblock, list a possible solution.

6. Explain why abstinence from alcohol and drugs is necessary for your recovery from both disorders.

7. List at least three things you could do to promote your recovery from your chemical dependency. Do the same for your PTSD.

8. Describe any concerns you may have about taking non-addictive medication for your PTSD.

9. Describe several ways that counseling or therapy could help your recovery.

10. Describe the qualities you want in a therapist who is working with you on these issues.

APPENDIX B

DAILY SCHEDULE

U se the chart on the next page as a model to develop your daily schedule one week at a time. Block out the times for specific activities and jot down the name of the activity in that block. Include your work, play, and interpersonal activities as well as your recovery activities. You need not account for every minute, but avoid large blocks of unscheduled time. Should such open blocks appear, plan pro-recovery activities for them. Review your plan daily and make adjustments as necessary. Place time in your schedule for rest too. The goal is balance and structure. Avoid too many blocks of unstructured time or too much activity. Self-care is essential to quality recovery from PTSD and addiction.

Daily Schedule

Week of _____

	Sun.	Mon.	Tues.	Wed.	Thurs.	Fri.	Sat.
AM 8							
9							
10							
11							
12							
PM 1							
2							
3							
4							
5							
6							
7							
8							
9							
10							
11							

TWELVE STEP SLOGANS

- Easy does it
- This, too, shall pass
- One day at a time
- First things first
- Turn it over
- Just for today
- Surrender
- More will be revealed
- You're right where you're supposed to be
- Fake it 'til you make it
- You're better than you think you are
- The paralysis of analysis
- Progression not perfection
- Let go and let God
- Stinking thinking
- Only one drink away from a drunk
- Powerless over people, places, and things
- Keep it simple
- God works through people
- Live in the solution not the problem

- Live life on life's terms
- Live in today
- Thy will, not mine
- If you don't take that first drink, you can't get drunk
- One drink is too many, but a thousand are not enough
- Live and let live
- HALT, Hungry, Angry, Lonely, Tired
- Meeting makers make it

The Co-occurring Disorders Series is the definitive resource on chemical addiction combined with psychiatric illnesses. Formerly titled the Dual Diagnosis Series, it has been updated with new findings, redesigned for greater readability, and expanded with additional materials.

This informative pamphlet is a useful tool for people in all stages of recovery. Descriptions, definitions, and personal stories will help you recognize co-occurring disorders and begin your recovery program.

Katie Evans, Ph.D., NCACII, CADCII, has a doctoral degree in clinical psychology and is a board-certified alcohol and drug counselor. She is an international workshop presenter, staff trainer, and program consultant. She has written books, booklets, and other client material on the topic of co-occurring disorders.

OTHER RESOURCES ON THIS SUBJECT:

#2177 Understanding Post-traumatic Stress Disorder and Addiction workbook

#2185 Understanding Post-traumatic Stress Disorder and Addiction video

Hazelden

15251 Pleasant Valley Road
Center City, MN 55012-0176

1-800-328-9000
(Toll Free U.S. and Canada)
1-651-213-4000
(Outside the U.S. and Canada)
1-651-213-4590 (Fax)
www.hazelden.org

Order No. 2178

ISBN 978-1-59285-025-9

PREVENTING RELAPSE

Katie Evans, Ph.D.

Celena Chong

HAZELDEN

Revised
Formerly the Dual Diagnosis Series